TEN LITTLE RABBITS

by Virginia Grossman
illustrated by Sylvia Long

A TRUMPET CLUB SPECIAL EDITION

One lonely traveler riding on the plain.

Two graceful dancers asking for some rain.

Three busy messengers sending out the news.

Four clever trackers looking for some clues.

Five wise storytellers trying to keep warm.

Six nimble runners fleeing from a storm.

Seven merry mischief-makers playing hide-and-seek.

Eight patient anglers fishing in a creek.

Nine festive drummers beating on a drum.

Ten sleepy weavers knowing day is done.

SIOUX

1 The Plains tribes depended on buffalo for food, clothing, bedding, and housing materials. They followed the herds, moving camp when the buffalo moved to new grazing areas. Prior to acquiring the horse, these tribes used dog travois to carry wood, food, small children, and the elderly. Although the child in this illustration is pictured alone, she would actually be part of a large group traveling together.

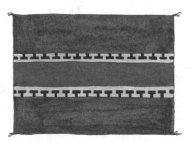

TEWA

2 Traditionally, all Rio Grande pueblos stage a corn dance, generally in the Spring. The dancers wear crimson parrot feathers and cowrie shells from the Pacific and carry gourd rattles. The male dancers leap and stamp to wake up the spirits. Finally, their evergreen finery (symbolic of the fir tree that, according to legend, people used to climb up from the underworld) is thrown in the river in the hope of pleasing the *Shiwana*, the rain-cloud people.

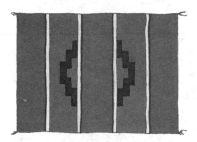

UTE

3 Plains tribes used smoke signals as a method of long-distance communication. Using a system of short and long puffs, they sent messages about such things as the presence of buffalo or the approach of enemies.

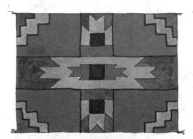

MENOMINEE

4 In the Great Lakes region, hunting bear had both practical and symbolic importance. Its fur was used for warmth, its flesh for food, and its fat was used as cooking oil, medicinal salves, and insect repellent. Its claws often made prize ornaments.

BLACKFOOT

5 Storytellers have always been a respected part of traditional Native American culture. They carried with them the legends, myths, and personal history of the tribe. In the oral tradition, this history had to be passed from one generation to the other by word of mouth.